Slimming World's
little book of
light bites

on a need-to-nibble basis

In Food Optimising, you've discovered the most delicious, healthy and satisfying way to lose weight, filling your plate (and your tummy) with Free Food whenever you feel hungry! That's the joy of Free Food. You really can fill up on it whenever you're hungry – day or night… even when a snack attack strikes!

❄ Recipes marked with this symbol can be frozen.

Ⓥ Recipes suitable for vegetarians have this symbol.

Whether it's a mid-morning must-have, a 'keep going till teatime' snack or something to share with family and friends for an evening in, we need a plan for when that most 'nibbly' moment comes! It's tempting at those times to reach for a high-Syn bite – the crisps, biscuits, nuts and chocolates that so easily take us off track and play havoc with our good intentions. And that's where this little book comes in!

It's packed with dozens of speedy and satisfying bite-size standbys that are easy to make. Some need no cooking at all and some are simple to cook in advance and keep in the fridge ready for those times. And best of all, almost *all* of them are Free! They're the healthy snacks that you *can* enjoy between meals and stay on plan!

They're filling, they're Free (or very low-Syn) and they're real Slimming World lifesavers!

Quick fixes

Our no-cook nibbles take 10 minutes or less to prepare so they're perfect when time is short. Every one of these sensational snacks is Free, too – so enjoy as many as you like!

ready in 10 minutes

makes 4

each wrap is:
Free on Extra Easy
Free on Original
3 Syns on Green

4 tbsp quark

juice of ½ lemon

salt and freshly ground
black pepper

4 large slices of lean
roast beef, visible fat
removed

small handful of rocket
leaves

1 tbsp balsamic vinegar

beef and rocket wraps

Mix the quark and lemon juice in a small bowl and season
well with salt and freshly ground black pepper.

Spread the mixture over one side of each slice of beef.
Top with the rocket leaves, drizzle with the balsamic
vinegar and roll up the beef slices. Grind over a little more
black pepper to taste.

Any you don't eat now will keep in the fridge for up to
2 days.

Free
on Extra Easy
and Original

ready in 10 minutes

makes 4

each stuffed tomato is:
Free on Extra Easy
Free on Original
1½ Syn on Green

160g can tuna steak in spring water or brine, drained

2 tbsp fat free natural fromage frais

2 spring onions, finely chopped

salt and freshly ground black pepper

4 tomatoes

tuna-stuffed tomatoes

Flake the tuna into a bowl and add the fromage frais and spring onions. Season with salt and freshly ground black pepper and mix together well.

Cut the tops off the tomatoes, scoop out and discard the seeds with a teaspoon and fill with the tuna mixture.

Any tomatoes you don't eat straight away will keep in the fridge for up to 2 days.

Depending on the size of your tomatoes, you might have some of the tuna mixture left over – it makes a delicious sandwich filling or crispbread topping too!

Free on Extra Easy and Original

ready in 5 minutes

the whole salad is:

Free on Extra Easy

Free on Green

10½ Syns on Original

410g can mixed beans or pulses, drained

small handful of finely chopped fresh parsley

2 tbsp fat free vinaigrette

salt and freshly ground black pepper

mixed bean
salad

Mix the beans or pulses with the parsley and vinaigrette in a bowl. Season with salt and freshly ground black pepper and mix together well.

Spoon as much salad as you feel like eating into a bowl. The rest will keep in the fridge for up to 4 days.

asian
prawn boats

each boat is:
Free on Extra Easy
Free on Original
1½ Syns on Green

100g cooked and
peeled prawns

3 tbsp soy sauce

3cm piece of root ginger,
peeled and grated

1 chilli, deseeded and
finely chopped

small handful of finely
chopped fresh coriander

1 Little Gem lettuce

Put the prawns, soy sauce, ginger, chilli and
coriander into a bowl and stir to mix well.

Spoon some of the mixture into a Little Gem leaf to eat.

Any you don't eat now will keep in the fridge
for up to 2 days.

*You can also make these tasty snacks
using the seafood selections available in
most supermarkets. They usually contain
prawns, squid and mussels.*

each cup is:
Free on Extra Easy
Free on Green
Free on Original

cucumber and
cottage cheese cups

½ cucumber

6 tbsp low fat natural cottage cheese

1 garlic clove, crushed

small handful of finely chopped fresh chives

salt and freshly ground black pepper

Cut the cucumber into 5cm thick slices. Using a teaspoon, scoop out and discard most of the seeds, leaving a thin layer at the base that will hold the filling.

Mix the cottage cheese, garlic and most of the chives in a small bowl. Season with salt and freshly ground black pepper and spoon the mixture into the cucumber cups. Scatter over the remaining chives and tuck in!

Any cups you don't eat straight away will keep in the fridge for up to 3 days.

Free
on
all choices

pastrami salad wraps

each wrap is:
Free on Extra Easy
Free on Original
½ **Syn** on Green

Mix the fromage frais, mustard powder and gherkins in a small bowl and spread over one side of the pastrami slices.

Top with the lettuce and roll up the pastrami slices.

Eat straight away or keep in the fridge for up to 2 days.

For a more indulgent version of this snack, use 4 tablespoons of extra-light mayonnaise instead of the fromage frais (1 extra Syn per wrap).

4 tbsp fat free natural fromage frais

½ tsp of mustard powder

4 gherkins, finely chopped

4 slices of pastrami, visible fat removed

4 lettuce leaves, shredded

Free on Extra Easy and Original

ready in 10 minutes

Free on Extra Easy
Free on Green
Free on Original

finely grated zest and
juice of 1 lemon

1 garlic clove, crushed

¼ tsp dried red chilli
flakes

1 tbsp finely chopped
fresh parsley

salt

400g can artichoke
hearts in water, drained
and halved

artichoke hearts
with garlic and lemon

Put the lemon zest and juice, garlic, chilli flakes, parsley
and salt in a bowl.

Add the artichokes and toss to mix well.

Anything you don't eat now will keep in the fridge for up to
4 days.

ready in 5 minutes

Free on Extra Easy

Free on Original

6 Syns on Green
(for 6 seafood sticks)

4 tbsp fat free natural fromage frais

1 garlic clove, crushed

½ tsp finely grated lemon zest

a few finely chopped fresh chives

as many seafood sticks as you like!

seafood
dippers

Put the fromage frais, garlic and most of the lemon zest and chives into a small bowl or ramekin and mix it all together well.

Scatter the remaining zest and chives over the sauce and dip in with as many seafood sticks as you like!

Free
on Extra Easy
and Original

ploughman's
on a stick

each stick is:
Free on Extra Easy
Free on Original
1½ **Syns** on Green

Cut each slice of ham into three long strips and roll up each strip tightly.

Thread the rolled-up ham strips on to four skewers or cocktail sticks along with the pickled onions.

Add a chunk of apple to any sticks you are eating straight away. Keep the rest in the fridge for up to 2 days and add the apple chunks when you are ready to eat.

4 thin slices of lean ham, visible fat removed

4 bottled silverskin pickled onions, drained

1 apple

Say cheese: You could add your favourite cheese to these ploughman's sticks by using a Healthy Extra 'a' choice or counting the Syns (eg 1 Babybel Light, halved or quartered, would be 2 Syns).

Free
on Extra Easy and Original

italian
tomato salad

ready in 10 minutes

Free on Extra Easy
Free on Green
Free on Original

Put the tomatoes in a ramekin or small bowl and add the balsamic vinegar, basil, garlic and chilli.

Season with salt and freshly ground black pepper and mix together well.

This salad is at its best eaten at room temperature so the flavour of the tomatoes really comes through.

8 cherry tomatoes, halved

1 tbsp balsamic vinegar

small handful of torn basil leaves

1 garlic clove, crushed

½ red chilli, deseeded and finely chopped

salt and freshly ground black pepper

Free
on
all choices

ready in 10 minutes

makes 4

each wrap is:

Free on Extra Easy

Free on Original

1½ Syns on Green

100g low fat natural
cottage cheese

small handful of roughly
chopped fresh dill, plus
extra to garnish

finely grated zest and
juice of 1 lemon

salt and freshly ground
black pepper

splash of Tabasco sauce
(optional)

4 slices of smoked
salmon

zesty smoked
salmon wraps

Put the cottage cheese, dill, lemon zest and juice in a bowl.
Season well with salt and freshly ground black pepper and
stir in the Tabasco if you want a snack with a kick.

Spread the cottage cheese mix over one side of the
smoked salmon slices, roll up the salmon and scatter over
the extra dill.

Eat straight away or keep in the fridge for up to 2 days.

Free
on Extra Easy
and Original

turkey and carrot wraps

ready in 10 minutes

makes 4

each wrap is:

Free on Extra Easy

Free on Original

2 Syns on Green

Put the carrot, yogurt and lemon juice in a bowl, season with salt and freshly ground black pepper and mix together well.

Spread the mixture over one side of each turkey slice, roll up the turkey slices and sprinkle over the paprika.

Eat straight away or keep in the fridge for up to 2 days.

1 carrot, coarsely grated

4 tbsp fat free natural yogurt

juice of 1 lemon

salt and freshly ground black pepper

4 large slices of lean cooked turkey breast, visible fat removed

½ tsp paprika

Free
on Extra Easy
and Original

ready in 10 minutes

Free on Extra Easy
Free on Green
Free on Original

1 apple, cored and diced

¼ cucumber, diced

small handful of roughly chopped fresh mint

juice of ½ lime

refresher salad

Put the apple, cucumber, mint and lime juice in a small bowl and mix well.

You could also make this fabulous fresh fix with a pear.

ready in 10 minutes

makes 4

each stick is:
Free on Extra Easy
Free on Original
1 Syn on Green

8 cooked and peeled
king or tiger prawns

2 bottled roasted
peppers in brine, drained
and cut into large pieces

1 tbsp roughly chopped
fresh dill

½ tsp dried red chilli
flakes (optional)

4 lemon wedges

chilli
prawn sticks

Thread the prawns and pepper pieces alternately on to
four skewers or cocktail sticks.

Sprinkle with the dill and chilli flakes (if you like a bit of heat).

Eat straight away with lemon wedges to squeeze over or
keep in the fridge for up to 2 days.

Deeply dippy

Our dips and pâtés are ideal for snacking because they're full of fantastic flavours and (unlike high fat supermarket options) they're *all* Free! Keep a bowl in your fridge and you'll be well stocked when hunger comes knocking!

ready in 20 minutes,
plus cooling and chilling

salmon
pâté

the whole pâté is:

Free on Extra Easy

Free on Original

26½ Syns on Green

200g skinless salmon
fillet

120g pack smoked
salmon (or use smoked
salmon trimmings)

3 tbsp fat free natural
yogurt

1 tsp lemon juice

small handful of fresh dill,
plus sprigs to garnish
(optional)

salt and freshly ground
black pepper

Put the salmon fillet in a small pan and cover with water.
Bring to the boil, reduce the heat to medium and simmer
for 10-12 minutes or until just cooked through. Drain well.

Meanwhile, put the smoked salmon, yogurt, lemon juice
and dill in a food processor. Flake in the cooked salmon
fillet, season well and whizz until roughly combined.

Spoon the pâté into a shallow bowl, garnish with dill sprigs,
if using, then cover, cool and chill for at least 1 hour.

Keep in the fridge for up to 2 days and serve with
crispbreads or your favourite crudités.

Free
on Extra Easy
and Original

ready in 25 minutes,
plus cooling

the whole pâté is:

Free on Extra Easy

Free on Green

Free on Original

mushroom
pâté

low calorie cooking spray

2 shallots, finely chopped

2 garlic cloves, finely chopped

250g mushrooms

1 tbsp fresh thyme leaves, plus sprigs to garnish (optional)

salt and freshly ground black pepper

150g quark

Spray a large non-stick frying pan with low calorie cooking spray and place over a high heat. Add the shallots and garlic and stir-fry for 5 minutes.

Meanwhile, tip the mushrooms into a food processor and blitz. Add the mushrooms to the pan along with the thyme and stir-fry for a further 10 minutes. Season well, remove from the heat and leave to cool slightly.

Clean the food processor, add the mushroom mixture and quark and blend until fairly smooth. Grind over a little black pepper and garnish with thyme sprigs if you like.

Cool and keep in the fridge for up to 3 days and serve with your favourite crudités or crispbreads.

Free on all choices

indian tarka
dhal dip

the whole dip is:

Free on Extra Easy

Free on Green

40 Syns on Original

Place the lentils in a large fine-mesh sieve and run cold water over them until the water runs clear. Drain well and place in a heavy-based saucepan with 1 litre of water. Bring to the boil over a high heat and skim away any scum that comes to the surface. Reduce the heat to medium and continue to cook for 20-25 minutes or until the lentils have softened.

Meanwhile, make the tarka. Spray a frying pan with low calorie cooking spray and place over a medium heat. When hot, add all the tarka ingredients and stir-fry for 1-2 minutes then remove from the heat and keep warm, setting aside the curry leaves.

Remove the lentils from the heat and blend until smooth using a stick blender. Return the pan to the heat, stir in the turmeric, tomatoes and tarka and simmer for another 2 minutes.

Season well and scatter over the fresh coriander and reserved curry leaves.

Cool and keep in the fridge for up to 4 days. This is delicious eaten with vegetable crudités.

250g dried red split lentils

1 tsp turmeric

4 tomatoes, roughly chopped

salt and freshly ground black pepper

large handful of finely chopped fresh coriander, to garnish

for the tarka

low calorie cooking spray

2 tsp black mustard seeds

3 tsp cumin seeds

2 garlic cloves, thinly sliced

2cm piece of root ginger, peeled and grated

8 fresh or dried curry leaves

1 tsp dried red chilli flakes

2 tsp ground cumin

2 tsp ground coriander

ready in 10 minutes

the whole dip is:

Free on Extra Easy

Free on Green

12½ Syns on Original

400g can chickpeas, drained

1 garlic clove, crushed

2 tbsp lemon juice, plus extra to taste

2 tbsp fat free natural Greek yogurt

salt and freshly ground black pepper

pinch of smoked paprika or cayenne pepper (optional)

speedy
houmous

Put the chickpeas, garlic, lemon juice and yogurt into a food processor and pulse until fairly smooth. Season with salt and freshly ground black pepper, add more lemon juice to taste and sprinkle with smoked paprika or cayenne pepper if you want a bit of extra spice.

Keep in the fridge for up to 3 days and serve with your favourite crudités or crispbreads.

Free on Extra Easy and Green

chicken liver pâté

the whole pâté is:

Free on Extra Easy

Free on Original

15½ Syns on Green

300g chicken livers, trimmed

low calorie cooking spray

1 celery stick, finely chopped

1 shallot, finely chopped

2 garlic cloves, finely chopped

a pinch of nutmeg

100g fat free natural fromage frais

salt and freshly ground black pepper

2 tbsp finely chopped fresh parsley

Rinse the chicken livers and pat them dry with kitchen paper.

Spray a large non-stick frying pan with low calorie cooking spray and place over a medium heat. Add the chicken livers, celery, shallot and garlic and stir-fry for 8-10 minutes.

Transfer the mixture to a food processor along with the nutmeg and fromage frais. Season well and process until fairly smooth, then transfer to a bowl and scatter over the parsley.

Cool and keep in the fridge for up to 2 days. This pâté is fantastic with crispbreads or vegetable crudités.

Free
on Extra Easy
and Original

ready in 40 minutes,
plus cooling

the whole dip is:

Free on Extra Easy

Free on Green

Free on Original

2 aubergines, halved
lengthways

2 red peppers, halved
lengthways

low calorie cooking spray

4 garlic cloves, crushed

1 tsp ground cumin

¼ tsp ground cinnamon

¼ tsp ground coriander

1 tsp smoked paprika

juice of 1 lemon

salt and freshly ground
black pepper

300g fat free natural
yogurt

large handful of roughly
chopped fresh coriander

spiced aubergine dip

Preheat the oven to 200°C/Fan 180°C/Gas 6.

Put the aubergines and red peppers into a roasting tin,
spray with low calorie cooking spray and roast for
20-25 minutes, turning once. Put the peppers in a
plastic food bag, seal and cool for 15 minutes.
Set the aubergines aside to cool slightly.

When the aubergines are cool enough to handle, scoop
the flesh into a food processor, discarding the skins.
Deseed and peel the peppers, then add the flesh to the
food processor along with the garlic, cumin, cinnamon,
ground coriander, paprika and lemon juice. Season well
and blend until fairly smooth. Add the yogurt and fresh
coriander and blend again briefly.

Cool and keep in the fridge for up to 3 days. This dip is
great with vegetable crudités or crispbreads.

Free
on
all choices

ready in 10 minutes

the whole dip is:
Free on Extra Easy
Free on Green
Free on Original

zippy tzatziki

½ cucumber, peeled, deseeded and grated

200g fat free natural Greek yogurt

2 garlic cloves, crushed

small handful of finely chopped fresh mint

1 tbsp lemon juice

salt and freshly ground black pepper

Put the cucumber, yogurt, garlic, mint and lemon juice in a bowl, season well and stir to mix all the flavours together.

Keep in the fridge for up to 3 days and serve with your favourite crispbreads or crudités.

ready in 45 minutes

the whole dip is:
Free on Extra Easy
Free on Green
Free on Original

butternut squash dip

800g peeled and diced butternut squash flesh

low calorie cooking spray

2 garlic cloves, crushed

juice of 1 lemon

1 tsp smoked paprika

salt and freshly ground black pepper

Preheat the oven to 200°C/Fan 180°C/Gas 6.

Spread out the squash on a non-stick baking sheet, spray lightly with low calorie cooking spray and roast for 25-30 minutes or until tender.

Transfer the squash to a food processor with the garlic, lemon juice and smoked paprika. Blend until fairly smooth, transfer to a bowl and season well.

Cool, keep in the fridge for up to 4 days and serve with vegetable crudités or crispbreads.

Make-ahead meaty

Cook a batch of these mouth-watering snacks and you'll have a fridge full of meaty moments or fishy favourites that will keep your appetite under wraps for days.

ready in 35 minutes,
plus chilling

makes 20

each meatball is:

Free on Extra Easy

Free on Original

1½ Syns on Green

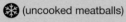 (uncooked meatballs)

500g extra-lean beef
mince

small handful of finely
chopped fresh coriander

1 tsp ground cumin

1 tsp ground coriander

1 tsp ground nutmeg

1 tsp ground cinnamon

3 garlic cloves, finely
chopped

salt and freshly ground
black pepper

low calorie cooking spray

small handful of finely
chopped fresh parsley

spanish meatballs

Put the mince, coriander, spices and garlic in a bowl.
Season and mix with your fingers until well combined.
Cover and chill in the fridge for 1 hour.

Divide the mince mixture into 20 portions and shape each
one into a bite-sized ball.

Spray a non-stick frying pan with low calorie cooking spray
and place over a medium heat. Stir-fry the meatballs for
6-8 minutes until browned and cooked through (you may
need to do this in two batches), then drain on kitchen paper.
Put the meatballs in a large serving dish and scatter with
the parsley.

These meatballs are great eaten straight away or you can
cool them and keep them in the fridge for up to 2 days.
They're delicious cold or thoroughly reheated – try them
with our quick garlic dip (page 82).

Free
on Extra Easy
and Original

ready in 15 minutes

the whole salad is:

Free on Extra Easy

7½ Syns on Green

34½ Syns on Original

200g dried pasta shapes

200g tenderstem broccoli, cut into bite-sized pieces

small bag of baby spinach leaves

low calorie cooking spray

4 lean bacon rashers, visible fat removed, roughly chopped

1 tsp dried chilli flakes

bacon and broccoli
pasta salad

Cook the pasta according to the packet instructions, adding the broccoli for the last 4 minutes and the spinach for the last 30 seconds. Drain well and tip into a serving bowl.

Meanwhile, spray a non-stick frying pan with low calorie cooking spray and place over a medium heat. Add the bacon and stir-fry for 3-4 minutes or until golden. Stir in the chilli flakes and cook for 2 minutes more, then add to the pasta and mix well.

Eat some straight away or cool and keep in the fridge for up to 2 days. This salad is great eaten cold or thoroughly reheated.

A little bit of blue cheese goes a long way in this dish! Divide the salad between plates and scatter over 25g diced dolcelatte (4½ Syns for the whole salad).

Free
on Extra Easy

ready in 45 minutes

makes 4

each drumstick is:

Free on Extra Easy

Free on Original

5½ Syns on Green

4 chicken drumsticks

5 tbsp fat free natural yogurt

2 tsp mild curry powder

1 tsp dried mint

½ tsp turmeric

finely grated zest and juice of ½ lime, plus wedges to serve

salt and freshly ground black pepper

curried chicken drumsticks

Skin the drumsticks by holding the bony end and pulling the skin over the thicker end (use a piece of kitchen paper to help you get a good grip). Discard the skin. With a sharp knife, make a few cuts in the flesh of each drumstick.

Put all the other ingredients in a wide bowl, season and mix well. Add the drumsticks, rubbing the mixture in to give a really good flavour. If you have time, cover and chill for 2 hours or preferably overnight.

Preheat the oven to 180°C/Fan 160°C/Gas 4.

Remove the drumsticks from the marinade, shaking off the excess, and bake for 35 minutes or until the chicken is cooked through. Turn them halfway through and spoon over any remaining marinade.

These are delicious eaten straight away or you can cool them and keep them in the fridge for up to 2 days. Eat cold or thoroughly reheated, with lime wedges to squeeze over.

ready in 40 minutes

makes 8

each skewer is:

Free on Extra Easy

Free on Original

4 Syns on Green

moussaka
skewers

large handful of finely
chopped fresh basil

juice of 2 lemons

1 tsp all-spice

1 tsp ground cumin

1 tsp ground cinnamon

1 tsp garlic salt

½ aubergine, cut into
bite-sized pieces

2 yellow peppers,
deseeded and cut into
bite-sized pieces

400g lean lamb leg steak,
visible fat removed, cut
into bite-sized cubes

low calorie cooking spray

8 cherry tomatoes

Mix together the basil, lemon juice, all-spice, cumin,
cinnamon and garlic salt in a wide bowl.

Preheat the oven to 200°C/Fan 180°C/Gas 6 and line
a baking sheet with non-stick baking parchment.

Add the aubergine, peppers and lamb to the spices in
the bowl, toss to coat evenly and spread out the mixture
on the prepared baking sheet. Lightly spray with low
calorie cooking spray and roast for 15-20 minutes or
until the lamb and vegetables are just tender.

Thread the lamb, roasted vegetables and cherry
tomatoes on to eight skewers or cocktail sticks.

Enjoy straight away or cool them and keep them in the
fridge for up to 2 days. Eat cold or thoroughly reheated.

Free
on Extra Easy
and Original

chinese duck
wraps

ready in 15 minutes

makes 4

each wrap is:

Free on Extra Easy

Free on Original

3½ Syns on Green

Put the duck strips in a bowl, sprinkle with the five spice powder, peppercorns and star anise and toss to coat.

Spray a non-stick wok or frying pan with low calorie cooking spray and place over a medium-high heat. Add the duck and stir-fry for 5 minutes or until cooked through.

To serve, fill a Little Gem leaf with a few slices of duck and a little spring onion, cucumber and chilli. The duck will keep in the fridge for up to 2 days and can be reheated thoroughly, if you like.

You can make this snack even tastier by serving it with a little hoisin, plum or sweet chilli sauce (all are ½ Syn per level teaspoon).

1 duck breast, skinned, visible fat removed, cut into thin strips

2 tsp Chinese five-spice powder

½ tsp ground mixed peppercorns

¼ tsp ground star anise

low calorie cooking spray

1 Little Gem lettuce

1 spring onion, shredded

¼ cucumber, cut into matchsticks

1 red chilli, deseeded and thinly sliced

Free
on Extra Easy
and Original

make-ahead meaty 65

chicken and tarragon frittata

ready in 25 minutes, plus standing

makes 6 slices

each slice is:

Free on Extra Easy

Free on Original

4 Syns on Green

low calorie cooking spray

half a bunch of spring onions, finely sliced or chopped

1 red pepper, deseeded and diced

6 large eggs

2 garlic cloves, crushed

small handful of finely chopped fresh tarragon or 2 tsp dried tarragon

salt and freshly ground black pepper

2 cooked skinless and boneless chicken breasts, roughly shredded

Preheat the grill to medium-high.

Spray a non-stick frying pan with low calorie cooking spray and place over a medium heat, then add the spring onions and red pepper and stir-fry for 4-5 minutes.

Meanwhile, beat the eggs in a bowl with the garlic then stir in the tarragon and season well. Pour this mixture into the frying pan and scatter the shredded chicken over the top. Cook gently for 5 minutes until the base is starting to set, then pop the pan under the grill for 4 minutes or until the top is set and golden. Remove from the heat and leave to stand for 10 minutes before slicing.

Enjoy some straight away or cool and keep in the fridge for up to 2 days. This frittata is fantastic eaten cold or thoroughly reheated.

Free on Extra Easy and Original

ready in 15 minutes

makes 8

each asparagus tip is:

Free on Extra Easy

Free on Original

1½ Syns on Green

8 asparagus tips or trimmed spears

8 thin slices of lean ham, visible fat removed

salt and freshly ground black pepper

low calorie cooking spray

ham-wrapped asparagus tips

Preheat the oven to 180°C/Fan 160°C/Gas 4 and line a baking sheet with non-stick baking parchment.

Cook the asparagus for 1-2 minutes in a large saucepan of lightly salted boiling water. Drain well, wrap a slice of ham tightly around each asparagus tip and place on the prepared baking sheet. Season well, spray lightly with low calorie cooking spray and bake for 5-6 minutes or until the ham is lightly browned and the asparagus is just tender.

These are delicious eaten straight away or you can cool them and keep in the fridge for up to 2 days. They can be eaten cold or thoroughly reheated.

Free
on Extra Easy
and Original

ready in 20 minutes

the whole salad is:
Free on Extra Easy
8½ Syns on Green
34½ Syns on Original

200g dried pasta shapes

100g sliced runner beans

low calorie cooking spray

2 spring onions, finely chopped

6 tbsp boiling vegetable stock

100g quark

salt and freshly ground black pepper

1 garlic clove, crushed

a pinch of nutmeg

juice of ½ lemon

small handful of finely chopped fresh dill

120g pack smoked salmon, cut into strips (or use smoked salmon trimmings)

smoked salmon pasta salad

Cook the pasta according to the packet instructions, adding the runner beans for the last 4 minutes. Drain and set aside.

Meanwhile, spray a large non-stick frying pan with low calorie cooking spray and place over a medium heat. Fry the spring onions for 1 minute then add the stock, turn the heat to high and boil for 2 minutes.

Stir in the quark, season well and add the garlic and nutmeg. Bring back to the boil then turn the heat to low and simmer for 2 minutes or until slightly thickened. Stir in the lemon juice and dill.

Add the pasta and beans to the sauce and stir to coat well. Fold in the smoked salmon and transfer to a serving bowl.

Eat some straight away if you like or cool and keep in the fridge for up to 2 days.

Free on Extra Easy

turkey and bacon ranch wraps

each wrap is:
Free on Extra Easy
Free on Original
3½ Syns on Green

Preheat the grill to high.

Grill the bacon for 3-4 minutes each side or until cooked to your liking. Drain on kitchen paper and cut into strips.

Meanwhile, mix all the ranch sauce ingredients in a small bowl, season well and spread over one side of the turkey slices.

Divide the pepper, tomato and bacon bits between the turkey slices, sprinkle with the paprika and roll up each one (you might need to hold them in place with cocktail sticks).

Enjoy straight away or cool and keep in the fridge for up to 2 days.

4 lean bacon rashers, visible fat removed

4 lean cooked turkey breast slices, visible fat removed

1 green pepper, halved, deseeded and sliced

1 tomato, deseeded and roughly chopped

1 tsp paprika

for the ranch sauce

150g fat free natural fromage frais

small handful of finely chopped fresh parsley and dill

1 garlic clove, crushed

1 tsp white wine vinegar

salt and freshly ground black pepper

Free on Extra Easy and Original

indian-spiced
chicken nuggets

ready in 30 minutes

makes 12

each nugget is:

Free on Extra Easy

Free on Original

2½ Syns on Green

❄ (uncooked nuggets)

Put the chicken in a food processor with the ginger, garlic, fennel seeds, cinnamon, curry powder and turmeric. Season and blend until fairly smooth. Turn out the mixture on to a clean work surface and divide into 12 equal portions. Roll each one into a little ball and flatten slightly to make nuggets.

Spray a large non-stick frying pan with low calorie cooking spray and place over a medium heat. Fry the nuggets for 6-7 minutes or until nicely browned, turning halfway (you may need to do this in batches).

Eat straight away with lemon wedges to squeeze over. You can also cool and keep them in the fridge for up to 2 days, enjoying them cold or thoroughly reheated.

The perfect accompaniment for these spicy nuggets is a little mango chutney (1 level teaspoon is ½ Syn).

5 skinless and boneless chicken thighs, visible fat removed, roughly chopped

2cm piece of root ginger, peeled and finely grated

1 garlic clove, crushed

1 tsp fennel seeds, crushed

½ tsp ground cinnamon

1 tbsp curry powder

1 tsp turmeric

salt and freshly ground black pepper

low calorie cooking spray

lemon wedges, to serve

Free
on Extra Easy and Original

minted lamb
couscous salad

the whole salad is:
Free on Extra Easy
15½ Syns on Green
26 Syns on Original

Preheat the oven to 200°C/Fan 180°C/Gas 6.

Put all the marinade ingredients in a large bowl and mix together.

Add the lamb, courgette, peppers and red onion to the marinade and stir to coat well. Tip everything into a roasting tin, spray with low calorie cooking spray and roast for 25 minutes.

Meanwhile, put the couscous in a heatproof bowl and pour over enough boiling water to just cover. Set aside, covered, for about 10 minutes or until the water is absorbed and the grains are tender. Run a fork through the couscous to fluff up the grains.

Set the lamb aside to rest for 10 minutes then roughly chop and fold into the couscous with the roasted vegetables. Scatter over the mint.

Eat some straight away or cool and keep in the fridge for up to 2 days. This salad is great eaten cold or thoroughly reheated in a microwave.

200g lean lamb leg steak, visible fat removed

1 courgette, diced

1 red and 1 yellow pepper, deseeded and cut into small pieces

1 red onion, cut into 6 wedges

low calorie cooking spray

150g dried couscous

small handful of finely chopped fresh mint

for the marinade

3 tbsp lemon juice

3 garlic cloves, crushed

1 tsp ground cumin

1 tsp ground cinnamon

2 tbsp balsamic vinegar

2 tbsp tomato purée

4 tbsp passata

Free
on Extra Easy

each kebab is:

Free on Extra Easy

Free on Original

2 Syns on Green

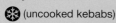 (uncooked kebabs)

300g peeled raw king or tiger prawns

1 lemon grass stick, outer leaves removed, roughly chopped

large handful of fresh coriander

small handful of fresh mint

1 tbsp soy sauce

2cm piece of root ginger, peeled and roughly chopped

2 garlic cloves, crushed

½ red chilli, deseeded and roughly chopped

2 tsp Thai fish sauce (nam pla)

low calorie cooking spray

thai prawn kebabs

Put the prawns, lemon grass, herbs, soy sauce, ginger, garlic, chilli and Thai fish sauce into a food processor and blitz to a rough paste. Transfer the mixture to a bowl.

With wet hands, divide the prawn mixture into six equal portions and shape each one into a kebab.

Place a non-stick frying pan over a medium heat and spray with low calorie cooking spray. Cook the kebabs for about 7-8 minutes, turning once or twice, until browned and just cooked through. (Alternatively, cook them under a medium-hot grill for 7 minutes.)

Eat straight away or cool and keep in the fridge for up to 2 days. These can be eaten cold or thoroughly reheated.

These kebabs are fantastic with sweet chilli sauce (½ Syn per level teaspoon).

Free on Extra Easy and Original

Make-ahead veggie

Our round-up of meat-free munches includes Bombay veg bites, Tex-Mex omelettes and more-ish sweetcorn fritters. Grazing has never been so much fun!

ready in 45 minutes

the whole recipe is:
Free on Extra Easy
Free on Green
22½ Syns on Original

1 tsp smoked paprika

2 tsp cumin seeds

1 tsp ground cinnamon

2 sweet potatoes,
scrubbed or peeled
and cut into wedges

low calorie cooking spray

for the garlic dip

200g quark

200g fat free fromage frais

1 garlic clove, crushed

1 tbsp cider vinegar

salt and freshly ground
black pepper

2 spring onions, finely
chopped

sweet potato wedges
with garlic dip

Preheat your oven to 200°C/Fan 180°C/Gas 6 and line a
large baking tray with non-stick baking parchment.

Mix the paprika, cumin seeds and cinnamon in a bowl,
spray the wedges with low calorie cooking spray and toss
them in the spices to coat evenly. Arrange them on the
baking tray and bake for 30 minutes or until tender.

Make the dip. Mix the quark, fromage frais, garlic and vinegar
in a bowl, season and sprinkle over the spring onions.

Sprinkle the wedges with salt and eat straight away with
the garlic dip. You can also cool the wedges and the dip
and keep in the fridge for up to 3 days, reheating the
wedges thoroughly before eating.

Free
on Extra Easy
and Green

ready in 30 minutes,
plus marinating

makes 8

each stick is:
Free on Extra Easy
Free on Green
Free on Original

2 tbsp tomato purée

2 tbsp passata

2 tbsp dark soy sauce

a splash of Tabasco sauce

½ tsp mustard powder

a pinch of sweetener

salt and freshly ground
black pepper

2 frozen low-fat Quorn
sausages

16 prepared fresh
pineapple chunks

small handful of finely
chopped fresh parsley

bbq sausage and
pineapple sticks

Mix the purée, passata, soy sauce, Tabasco sauce,
mustard powder and sweetener in a shallow bowl.
Season, add the sausages and toss to coat evenly.
Cover and chill for 4 hours or overnight if time permits.

When you're ready to cook, preheat the oven to
200°C/Fan 180°C/Gas 6.

Bake the sausages for 20-25 minutes, then cut each
sausage into four pieces and thread each piece on to a
cocktail stick along with a couple of pineapple chunks.
Scatter with parsley.

Eat straight away or cool and keep in the fridge for up to
2 days. These are great eaten cold.

*For extra flavour add ½ teaspoon of
Worcestershire sauce to the sausage marinade
(but remember the sticks won't be vegetarian).*

ready in 40 minutes

makes 6 slices

each slice is:
Free on Extra Easy
Free on Green
1 Syn on Original

1 large potato, peeled and diced

low calorie cooking spray

2 courgettes, thinly sliced

1 garlic clove, finely chopped

small handful of finely chopped fresh mint

4 eggs, beaten

salt and freshly ground black pepper

Free
on Extra Easy and Green

minted courgette
tortilla

Boil the potatoes for 5 minutes or until just tender, then drain well.

Spray a large, ovenproof frying pan with low calorie cooking spray and place over a medium-low heat. Stir-fry the courgettes for 5 minutes until they start to soften. Turn the heat up to medium, add the potatoes and garlic and fry for 8-10 minutes, turning the vegetables occasionally, until the potatoes begin to go golden.

Preheat your grill to medium.

Put the mint and eggs in a bowl, season and beat in 2 tablespoons of water. Add the eggs to the vegetables in the pan and turn the heat to medium-low. Cook for 7-8 minutes or until the eggs are almost set.

Put the pan under the grill and cook for 5 minutes or until cooked through. Leave the tortilla to stand for 2 minutes, then loosen the edges with a palette knife. Season well and cut into slices.

Have some straight away or cool and keep in the fridge for up to 3 days. Eat cold or thoroughly reheated.

griddled aubergine rolls

First mix the filling ingredients in a bowl. Season well and set aside.

Slice off and discard the aubergine ends, then slice lengthways into eight thin strips and season to taste.

Heat a non-stick griddle over a high heat until smoking hot and spray the aubergine slices with low calorie cooking spray. Griddle the slices for 1-2 minutes on each side, then place the slices on a clean work surface. You may need to do this in batches.

Place a tablespoonful of the filling at one end of an aubergine slice. Roll it up tightly, starting from the filling end. Repeat until you've used up all of the aubergine and filling.

Sprinkle with parsley and eat straight away or cool and keep in the fridge for up to 3 days. These are great eaten cold.

Free on all choices

ready in 45 minutes

makes 8 rolls

each roll is:
Free on Extra Easy
Free on Green
Free on Original

1 aubergine

low calorie cooking spray

small handful of finely chopped fresh parsley, to garnish

for the filling

100g quark

1 bottled roasted red pepper in brine, drained and chopped

1 garlic clove, crushed

large handful of finely chopped fresh coriander

finely grated zest of ½ lime

salt and freshly ground black pepper

chinese vegetable cups

ready in 20 minutes, plus cooling

makes 4

each cup is:
Free on Extra Easy
Free on Green
Free on Original

Spray a non-stick wok or frying pan with low calorie cooking spray and place over a medium-high heat.

Add the stir-fry vegetables, chilli, ginger and garlic and fry for 5-6 minutes or until everything is just cooked but still deliciously crunchy.

Remove from the heat, add the soy sauce and drain in a colander. Allow the mixture to cool completely then transfer to a serving bowl and keep in the fridge for up to 4 days.

When you're feeling hungry, fill a Little Gem lettuce leaf with some of the vegetable mixture and tuck in.

low calorie cooking spray

150g mixed stir-fry vegetables

1 red chilli, deseeded and finely chopped

1cm piece of root ginger, peeled and finely chopped

2 garlic cloves, crushed

2 tbsp soy sauce or to taste

1 Little Gem lettuce

Free on all choices

caribbean
rice salad

ready in 20 minutes

the whole salad is:
Free on Extra Easy
Free on Green
35 Syns on Original

Cook the rice according to the packet instructions. Drain, rinse under cold running water and transfer to a serving bowl.

Mix the remaining ingredients into the rice and season to taste.

Eat straight away with lime wedges or keep in the fridge for up to 1 day. When you're feeling peckish, spoon some rice salad into a ramekin or small bowl and serve cold.

200g dried basmati rice

100g prepared fresh mango chunks, diced

100g prepared fresh pineapple chunks, diced

½ cucumber, diced

1 red chilli, deseeded and finely chopped

½ red onion, finely chopped

small handful of finely chopped fresh mint

salt and freshly ground black pepper

lime wedges, to serve

Free
on Extra Easy
and Green

ready in 10 minutes,
plus soaking

makes 4

each cobette is:

Free on Extra Easy

Free on Green

5 Syns on Original

finely grated zest and
juice of 1 lime

1 red chilli, deseeded
and finely chopped

small handful of finely
chopped fresh coriander
and parsley

1 tsp sea salt

4 sweetcorn cobettes

chilli sweetcorn
cobettes

Preheat the grill to medium-hot and soak four wooden
skewers in water for 20 minutes (this stops them burning
under the grill).

Meanwhile, put the lime zest and juice, chilli, coriander,
parsley and salt in a bowl and stir.

Thread each cobette on to one of the soaked wooden
skewers and grill for 5-6 minutes, turning a few times, and
brush the marinade over the cobettes for the final minute
of the cooking time.

Enjoy straight away or cool the cobettes and keep in the
fridge for up to 4 days. These are amazing eaten cold or
thoroughly reheated.

ready in 40 minutes

makes 6

each muffin is:

Free on Extra Easy

Free on Green

Free on Original

low calorie cooking spray

200g asparagus tips, cut into small pieces

1 bottled roasted red pepper in brine, drained and finely chopped

6 large eggs

2 garlic cloves, crushed

small handful of finely chopped fresh tarragon

salt and freshly ground black pepper

Free on all choices

asparagus and roasted pepper muffins

Preheat the oven to 180°C/Fan 160°C/Gas 4.

Lightly spray a non-stick six-hole silicone muffin tray with low calorie cooking spray. If you don't have one, line a regular muffin tray with paper cases and spray them with low calorie cooking spray.

Blanch the asparagus in a saucepan of lightly salted boiling water for 1-2 minutes. Drain, pat dry with kitchen paper and divide the asparagus and roasted red pepper between the muffin holes.

Beat the eggs and stir in the garlic and tarragon. Season well and carefully spoon the egg mixture into the muffin holes. Bake for 20-25 minutes or until set and golden then leave to stand for 10 minutes.

Run a small palette knife around the muffins and carefully ease them out.

Enjoy straight away or cool and keep in the fridge for up to 3 days and eat cold or thoroughly reheated.

ratatouille
on a stick

ready in 35 minutes

makes 16

each stick is:
Free on Extra Easy
Free on Green
Free on Original

Preheat the oven to 200°C/Fan 180°C/Gas 6.

Put the aubergine and courgette pieces into a baking tray. Scatter over the oregano, season well and spray with low calorie cooking spray. Roast for about 10 minutes then add the cherry tomatoes to the baking tray and roast for another 10-15 minutes or until everything is nicely browned and cooked through.

Thread the vegetables and basil leaves on to skewers or cocktail sticks. Enjoy some straight away or cool and keep in the fridge for up to 4 days.

½ aubergine, cut into bite-sized pieces

1 courgette, cut into bite-sized pieces

1 tbsp dried oregano

salt and freshly ground black pepper

low calorie cooking spray

32 cherry tomatoes

large handful of fresh basil leaves

Free
on
all choices

ready in 50 minutes

makes 12

each potato is:

Free on Extra Easy

Free on Green

1½ Syns on Original

12 salad potatoes, such as Charlotte

salt and freshly ground black pepper

low calorie cooking spray

mini jacket
potatoes

Preheat the oven to 220°C/Fan 200°C/Gas 7.

Prick the potatoes all over with a fork and arrange them on a baking sheet. Season well and lightly spray with low calorie cooking spray.

Bake on the top shelf of the oven for 20 minutes. Turn the heat down to 190°C/Fan 170°C/Gas 5 and bake for a further 25-30 minutes or until the skins are crisp and the flesh is soft.

Cool and keep in the fridge for up to 4 days. To eat, reheat thoroughly then halve and add your favourite topping.

Tempting topping ideas

♡ Sweetcorn kernels mixed with diced roasted red pepper, red onion, coriander and lime juice.

♡ Spiced baked beans (page 109) with a dollop of fromage frais.

♡ Red kidney beans canned in mild chilli sauce.

ready in 35 minutes

Free on Extra Easy

Free on Green

Free on Original

300g chantenay carrots, trimmed and halved lengthways

2 fennel bulbs, trimmed, quartered and thickly sliced

low calorie cooking spray

salt and freshly ground black pepper

finely grated zest of 1 orange

small handful of finely chopped fresh dill

roasted fennel
and carrot chips

Preheat the oven to 200°C/Fan 180°C/Gas 6 and line a large roasting tin with non-stick baking parchment.

Place the carrot and fennel pieces in a single layer in the roasting tin and lightly spray with low calorie cooking spray. Season well and roast for 25 minutes or until the vegetables begin to turn lightly golden, turning once.

Remove from the oven and scatter over the orange zest and dill.

Eat some straight away or cool and keep in the fridge for up to 4 days. These scrumptious chips are great eaten cold or thoroughly reheated.

ready in 25 minutes

makes 4

each omelette wrap is:
Free on Extra Easy
Free on Green
Free on Original

low calorie cooking spray

1 red pepper, halved, deseeded and finely sliced

1 yellow pepper, halved, deseeded and finely sliced

3 shallots, halved and finely sliced

2 garlic cloves, crushed

1 tsp ground cumin

small handful of roughly chopped fresh coriander

6 eggs

½ red chilli, deseeded and finely chopped

lime wedges, to serve

tex-mex
omelette wraps

Spray a non-stick frying pan with low calorie cooking spray and place over a medium-high heat. Add the peppers, shallots, garlic and cumin and stir-fry for 4-5 minutes then put the mixture into a bowl and scatter over the coriander. Wipe the pan with kitchen paper and spray with low calorie cooking spray.

Lightly beat the eggs in a large measuring jug and stir in the chilli. Pour one-quarter of the egg mixture into the pan and tilt it around. Cook for 1½ minutes on each side or until the edges turn golden then loosen with a palette knife and slide on to greaseproof paper. Repeat to make three more omelettes.

Spoon the vegetables on to the omelettes and roll them up. They're now ready to eat – or you can cool them and keep them in the fridge for up to 3 days. Enjoy cold or thoroughly reheated, with lime wedges to squeeze over.

Free on all choices

ready in 40 minutes

Free on Extra Easy
Free on Green
Free on Original

½ cauliflower head, cut into bite-sized florets

¼ butternut squash, peeled, deseeded and cut into bite-sized chunks

2 red peppers, halved, deseeded and cut into bite-sized pieces

2 garlic cloves, crushed

1 tbsp mild curry powder

1 tsp cumin seeds

1 tsp black mustard seeds

1 tsp dried chilli flakes

2 tsp dried mint

juice of 2 lemons

salt and freshly ground black pepper

low calorie cooking spray

fat free natural yogurt sprinkled with paprika, to serve

bombay veg bites

Preheat the oven to 200°C/Fan 180°C/Gas 6 and line a roasting tin with non-stick baking parchment.

Add the cauliflower, squash and peppers to the roasting tin. Sprinkle over the garlic, spices, mint and lemon juice and season well. Lightly spray with low calorie cooking spray and roast for 20-25 minutes, turning halfway, until lightly browned but still deliciously crunchy.

Snack on these tasty bites straight away or cool them and keep them in the fridge for up to 4 days. They're sensational eaten cold or thoroughly reheated, served with fat free yogurt sprinkled with paprika.

Free
on all choices

spiced baked beans

the whole recipe is:
Free on Extra Easy
Free on Green
27 Syns on Original

Place a large non-stick saucepan over a medium-high heat and spray with low calorie cooking spray. Add the onion and garlic and stir-fry for 3-4 minutes.

Add all the remaining ingredients, season well and bring to the boil. Cover, reduce the heat to medium and cook for 12-15 minutes, stirring often.

Check the seasoning, remove from the heat and scatter over the fresh herbs.

These beans are most delicious eaten hot so if you don't eat them all straight away, cool and keep in the fridge for up to 4 days. Reheat thoroughly to serve.

low calorie cooking spray

1 onion, finely chopped

2 garlic cloves, crushed

415g can baked beans in tomato sauce

410g can mixed beans or pulses

4 tbsp tomato purée

1 bay leaf

1 tsp smoked paprika

1 red chilli, deseeded and finely chopped

salt and freshly ground black pepper

small handful of roughly chopped fresh coriander or parsley, to garnish

Free
on Extra Easy and Green

fruity coleslaw

Put the cabbage, carrot, radishes, apple, peach, cucumber and spring onions into a large bowl.

Mix the dressing ingredients in a small bowl and pour over the vegetables and fruit.

Season to taste and mix well. This coleslaw will keep in the fridge for up to 2 days, so scoop some into a small bowl whenever hunger hits.

Free
on all choices

ready in 20 minutes

Free on Extra Easy
Free on Green
Free on Original

½ white cabbage, shredded

1 carrot, peeled and shredded

8 radishes, thinly sliced

1 apple, halved, cored and cut into matchsticks

1 peach, halved, stoned and cut into matchsticks

½ cucumber, halved, deseeded and cut into matchsticks

bunch of spring onions, sliced

salt and freshly ground black pepper

for the dressing

5 tbsp fat free vinaigrette

juice of 2 limes

1 tsp Chinese five-spice powder

courgettes
with mustard seeds

Free on Extra Easy
Free on Green
Free on Original

Preheat the oven to 200°C/Fan 180°C/Gas 6 and line a large roasting tin with non-stick baking parchment.

Arrange the courgette slices in a single layer in the roasting tin and sprinkle over the spices, salt and lemon juice. Lightly spray with low calorie cooking spray and roast for 20-25 minutes or until tender.

Eat straight away or cool them and keep them in the fridge for up to 4 days. Eat cold or thoroughly reheated.

You can also make this snack with a marrow – just cut it into six thick slices and deseed, then scatter over the spices, salt and lemon juice and cook as above.

2 large courgettes, thickly sliced diagonally

2 tsp nigella seeds

2 tsp mustard seeds

1 tsp dried red chilli flakes

salt

juice of 1 lemon

low calorie cooking spray

Free
on
all choices

make-ahead veggie 113

ready in 15 minutes

the whole salad is:
Free on Extra Easy
Free on Green
39 Syns on Original

herby pasta
salad

200g dried pasta
shapes

150g frozen petit pois

2 bottled roasted red
peppers in brine,
roughly chopped

1 orange pepper,
deseeded and roughly
chopped

grated zest and juice of
1 unwaxed lemon

small handful of finely
chopped fresh parsley

small handful of finely
chopped fresh mint

5 tbsp fat free
vinaigrette

salt and freshly ground
black pepper

Cook the pasta according to the packet instructions,
adding the peas for the final 2 minutes of the cooking time.
Drain, rinse under cold running water and drain again.

Meanwhile, put all the remaining ingredients into a salad
bowl. Add the cooked pasta and peas, season and mix
well to bring all the flavours together.

Eat some straight away or keep in the fridge for up to
3 days. This salad is best eaten cold.

ready in 50 minutes

Free on Extra Easy
Free on Green
Free on Original

as many cherry tomatoes
as you like, halved

salt and freshly ground
black pepper

dried oregano or thyme
– 2 tsp for every 8
tomatoes

slow-roasted
cherry tomatoes

Preheat the oven to 140°C/Fan 120°C/Gas 1.

Put the tomato halves in a roasting tin, cut side up.
Season well, scatter over the dried herbs and roast for
40-45 minutes or until they are starting to dry out –
this will really concentrate the flavour!

Eat some tomatoes straight away or cool and keep in the
fridge for up to 4 days. These are best eaten cold.

*This recipe works just as well with
bigger tomatoes, though you might
need to roast them for a little longer.*

ready in 20 minutes

makes 20

each fritter is:
Free on Extra Easy
Free on Green
½ **Syn** on Original

2 spring onions, trimmed

½ red chilli, deseeded and finely chopped

2 eggs

340g can sweetcorn kernels, drained

salt and freshly ground black pepper

small handful of finely chopped fresh chives

low calorie cooking spray

lime wedges, to serve

sweetcorn
and chive fritters

Put the spring onions, chilli, eggs and three-quarters of the sweetcorn in a food processor and blitz until combined. Season well and transfer to a large bowl, then add the chives and remaining sweetcorn and mix to combine.

Spray a large non-stick frying pan with low calorie cooking spray and place over a medium-high heat. When the pan is hot, drop in heaped tablespoons of the mixture and cook for 1-2 minutes each side or until lightly golden and cooked through. Drain on kitchen paper and repeat until you have used up all of the mixture.

Enjoy straight away with lime wedges or cool and keep in the fridge for up to 3 days. Eat cold or thoroughly reheated.

Free
on Extra Easy
and Green

Sweet savers

Sometimes snacks just have to be sweet – so if you're feeling fruity or think an ice would be nice, read on!

ready in 5 minutes,
plus standing

Free on Extra Easy

Free on Green

Free on Original

250g box strawberries, halved

1 tbsp balsamic vinegar

2 tsp sweetener (optional)

fat free natural fromage frais

freshly ground black pepper

balsamic
strawberries

Put the strawberries in a bowl and sprinkle over the balsamic vinegar and sweetener, if using. Toss to coat well, cover and leave to stand for at least 20 minutes to let the flavours mingle.

When you're ready for a snack, spoon some strawberries into a bowl, add a dollop of fat free fromage frais and grind over some black pepper. The strawberries will keep in the fridge for up to 2 days.

Free
on
all choices

ready in 10 minutes, plus freezing

makes 8

each lolly is:

Free on Extra Easy

Free on Green

Free on Original

350ml diet lemonade

2 tbsp sweetener

small handful of finely chopped fresh mint

zest and juice of 1 lime

mojito
ice lollies

Put the lemonade in a jug and stir in the sweetener, mint, lime zest and juice.

Pour the lemonade mixture into 8 x 50ml ice-lolly moulds, insert an ice lolly stick into each mould and freeze for 8-10 hours or until firm.

When you need a sweet treat, turn out a lolly from its mould and enjoy!

If you don't have a lolly stick attachment for your moulds, you can still hold the sticks in place while the lollies freeze. Fix a sheet of tin foil over the top of the moulds, make small slits with a knife and gently push in the lolly sticks.

Free
on
all choices

sweet banana pot

ready in 5 minutes

Free on Extra Easy

Free on Green

Free on Original

Ⓥ

Mix the yogurt and sweetener in a ramekin or small bowl and stir in the banana.

Dust with a little nutmeg or cinnamon to eat.

3 tbsp fat free natural yogurt

1 tsp sweetener, or to taste

1 banana, sliced

grated nutmeg or a pinch of cinnamon

For an extra-sweet treat, add 1 level teaspoon of runny honey (1 Syn).

Free on all choices

Free on Extra Easy

Free on Green

Free on Original

1 ripe mango

¼ honeydew melon, seeded

¼ cantaloupe melon, seeded

juice of 1 lime

1 tbsp finely chopped fresh mint, to decorate

melon ball and mango salad

Peel and stone the mango then cut the flesh into cubes and put them in a large bowl.

Using a melon baller or teaspoon, make small balls from the melons and add the balls to the mango. Sprinkle over the lime juice and mint.

The salad is now ready to eat – or you can keep it in the fridge for up to 2 days.

raspberry and rosemary sorbet

the whole sorbet is:

5 **Syns** on Extra Easy

5 **Syns** on Green

5 **Syns** on Original

Put the frozen raspberries, yogurts and rosemary in a food processor and whizz until well blended. Scrape the mixture from the sides and whizz again until well combined.

Pour the mixture into a shallow, freezerproof container then cover and freeze for at least 1 hour or until just firm enough to scoop.

Scoop some sorbet into a chilled bowl or glass whenever you need a sweet snack.

400g frozen raspberries

4 x 175g pots Muller Light Raspberry & Cranberry yogurt (or use any Free raspberry yogurt)

½ tsp finely chopped fresh rosemary leaves

ready in 15 minutes

makes 4 (8 halves)

each peach half is:

Free on Extra Easy

Free on Green

Free on Original

4 ripe peaches

150g fat free natural fromage frais

3 tbsp quark

1 tsp finely grated lime zest and 2 tsp lime juice, plus extra zest to decorate

small handful of finely chopped fresh mint, plus sprigs to decorate

freshly ground black pepper

pinch of cinnamon, to decorate

italian stuffed peaches

Using a sharp knife, cut the peaches in half and carefully remove and discard the stones. Arrange on a plate, cut side up.

In a small bowl, whisk the fromage frais and quark until smooth then stir in the lime zest, juice and mint. Season with black pepper and mix well.

Spoon the mixture into the peach halves, sprinkle over a little cinnamon and lime zest and decorate with a mint sprig.

Eat some of the peaches straight away or keep them in the fridge for up to 2 days.

Free
on
all choices

ready in 5 minutes

makes 6

tropical fruit kebabs

each kebab is:

Free on Extra Easy

Free on Green

Free on Original

6 prepared fresh mango chunks

1 kiwi fruit, peeled and cut into 6 chunks

6 prepared fresh pineapple chunks

lime wedges, to serve

Thread a chunk each of mango, kiwi fruit and pineapple on to six skewers or cocktail sticks and keep them in the fridge for up to 2 days.

Squeeze the juice of 1 lime wedge over each fruit kebab just before eating.

ready in 10 minutes,
plus cooling and setting

makes 4

zesty
mini-trifles

each trifle is:

½ **Syn** on Extra Easy

½ **Syn** on Green

½ **Syn** on Original

11.5g sachet sugar-free
strawberry jelly crystals

2 x 175g pots Muller Light
Banana & Custard yogurts
(or use any Free banana
yogurt)

1 tbsp orange zest

1 level tsp cocoa powder

Make up the jelly according to the packet instructions and
set aside to cool.

Divide the cooled jelly between dessert glasses and leave
to set in the fridge for 6 hours or overnight.

Once the jelly is set, mix the yogurts and most of the
orange zest in a bowl and spoon the mixture into the
glasses. Sprinkle over the cocoa powder and remaining
orange zest.

These delicious trifles will keep in the fridge for up to
3 days.

orange, mint and pomegranate salad

Free on Extra Easy
Free on Green
Free on Original

4 large oranges

80g pomegranate seeds

juice of 1 lemon

freshly ground black pepper

small handful of roughly chopped fresh mint

Cut the top and bottom off each orange and carefully cut away the skin and pith. Slice the oranges horizontally, arrange the slices on a large plate and sprinkle over the pomegranate seeds.

Drizzle with the lemon juice, season with black pepper and scatter over the mint.

Eat some of the salad straight away or keep it in the fridge for up to 2 days.

Free
on
all choices

ready in 10 minutes,
plus freezing

makes 8

each ice pop is:

½ **Syn** on Extra Easy

½ **Syn** on Green

½ **Syn** on Original

2 level tbsp cocoa powder

2 tbsp sweetener

2 x 175g pots Muller Light
Vanilla yogurt (or use
any Free vanilla yogurt)

1 tsp vanilla extract

chocolate and
vanilla ice pops

Put the cocoa powder, half the sweetener and 3 tablespoons of water in a small bowl and stir well.

Put the yogurt in a small jug and stir in the vanilla extract and remaining sweetener.

Swirl the cocoa mixture through the yogurt and pour into 8 x 80ml dariole moulds or ice-lolly moulds. Insert an ice lolly stick into each mould and freeze for 8-10 hours or until firm.

Whenever you fancy a sweet treat, turn out an ice pop from its mould and enjoy!

If you don't have a lolly stick attachment for your moulds, you can still hold the sticks in place while the ice pops freeze. Fix a sheet of tin foil over the top of the moulds, make small slits with a knife and gently push in the lolly sticks.

index

Published in 2014 by
Slimming World
Clover Nook Road
Somercotes
Alfreton
Derbyshire
DE55 4SW
UK
www.slimmingworld.com

Created and designed by
Slimming World's publications team

Publications manager: Allison Brentnall
Editor: Oliver Maxey
Designer: Fabiana Viracca-Butler

Recipes and food styling: Sunil Vijayakar
Photographs: Gareth Morgans
Styling: Morag Farquhar

Front cover photograph: Sweet potato wedges with garlic dip, page 82